Dot on Men

Dot on Men

Everything you always wanted
to know about men
but were too bored to ask

Daphne David

Michael O'Mara Books Limited

First published in Great Britain in 1998
by Michael O'Mara Books Limited
9 Lion Yard
Tremadoc Road
London SW4 7NQ

A CIP catalogue record for this book is available from
the British Library

ISBN 1-85479-348-9

1 3 5 7 9 10 8 6 4 2

Designed by Mick Keates
Formatting by Concise Artisans
Printed and bound in Great Britain by
Cox & Wyman Ltd, Reading, Berks.

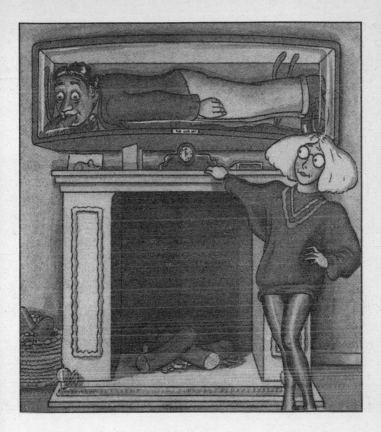

'Well!' Dot thought defensively,
'It's not everyday you find a man
who can cook and make love
like a donkey on roller-skates.'

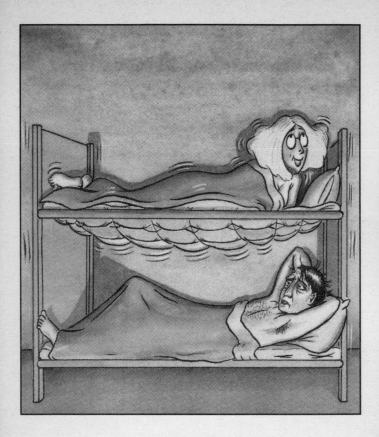

After a little practice,
Dot enjoyed being on top.

Dot and John had very
different ideas about what
made underwear 'sexy.'

'Look Gavin', said Dot, 'just
admit I'm the complete and
entire hub of your existance
and I'll admit I forgot
to do the washing'.

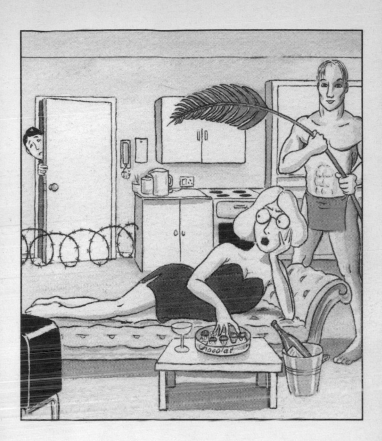

'Get out!' Shouted Dot.
"A woman's place is in
the kitchen." Isn't that
what you always said?'

One day Dot found an 'ex'
down the back of the sofa.

Dot found
emotionally unstable men
quite hard to handle.

A gentleman friend of Dot
took her to
a little bistro he knew.

Dot began to wonder
if she'd chosen the right
stress management course.

'I'm just popping out for a while,'
said Dot merrily, 'because you're
all getting on my tits.'

'But I fancy him!' Shrieked Dot,
as she dragged the handsome
stranger off the bus.

Dot followed the manufacturer's
instructions, and got to know
her washing machine. But she
made it quite clear 'sex was out'.

Dot was curious to know
if the workmen would still
whistle at her after she sawed
the legs off their scaffolding.

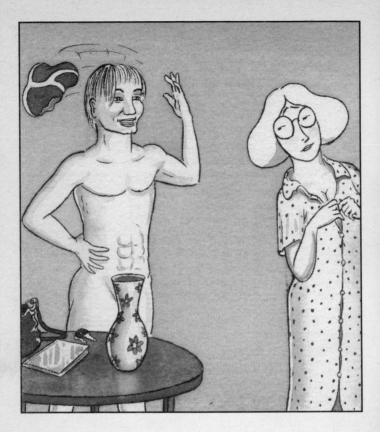

'Yow! Woof!' Thought Dot,
calmly. 'Not a bad
substitute for a brain'.

'Bollocks'. Muttered Dot.

'My diet is going fine,
thank you for asking'. Said Dot.
'Now piss off.'

'Oh for pity's sake,' growled Dot,
'there must be more to intimacy
than farting in bed.'

Dot expressed her anger
in a measured way when
she discovered George was
having an affair: 'You've been
a naughty boy haven't you?
Well, just pop your penis
on the sideboard.'

24

'So you've done the
washing-up!' Snapped Dot
'What do you want; the
Queen's Award for Industry?'

Dot solved the 'no condom' crisis
by snipping a finger out of
one of her Marigolds.

'I've made a sort of "either or" wish', Said Dot. 'Either you turn into a sexy hunk or you disappear.'

'You see', chuckled Dot,
'we women do have
a sense of humour.'

Finally Dot spoke: Shall we go
and see what's on telly —
it's more fun than trying to
push a marshmallow into
a slot-machine.

'Listen', hissed Dot, if you
ask the waitress to
describe the sausages
once more, you're going
to get this fish-fork in
your "meat and potatoes" ok!

Tim's devotion was beginning to
annoy Dot. 'For God's sake!'
She said. 'I threw the stick
for the dog.'

'For somebody who doesn't
care about winning', sneered
Dot, 'you're doing rather
a lot of celebrating.'

'No, wait!' Shrieked Dot.
'I've always wanted a reliable
father figure in my life.'

'No clean socks!? Well let me knit
you a pair!' Shrieked Dot.
'And perhaps you'd like to use
my body while you're waiting!'

'It's from a joke shop'. Said Dot,
'It saves me having to say
"I've got a headache"
all weekend'.

'For pity's sake, Lulu!' Wailed Dot.
'I know Christmas is the time
of goodwill to all men but...
you know... 3 at once?!?'

There were times when Dot
didn't mind Gavin looking
at other women.

Dot was impressed with
Howard's cleaning. 'Very good
Howie,' she purred, 'keep this up and
you could be on for a spot
of sex at the weekend.'

After Dot got home from work,
picked up the kids from school,
gave them tea, tidied the house,
vaccumed the garden and polished
the hamster, she could relax with
her book: 'How The Modern Woman
Has Become Free'.

'Here, hold the baby!' Snapped Dot.
Now you know what
"women's problems" are.'

Dot should've known Matt's competitive streak would turn a quick game of draughts into a 3 day event.

'Wow! Look where Dave gave me
a love bite last night'.
Said Lulu casually.

'Yes that's the tip' Said Dot.
'It's a fresh pound coin
on a bed of wild, small change'.

'Sorry Barry!' Shouted Dot.
'I got a better offer.'

After John's experiment
with 'dirty talk',
Dot found herself aroused
-but not sexually.

'Garry,' said Dot slowly,
'you know we've been living
together for a year now—
do you still have to keep
your clothes in a suitcase
by the door?'

Half way through the reception
Dot realised she wasn't
dreaming and passed out.

At dinner Dot found herself between two accountants who were into windsurfing.

'You're leaving me?!
Gulped Dot. 'Well actually,
Martin, I left you yesterday
and I just came out
tonight to tell you!'

Dot soon settled into her new job once she'd got her 'workspace' organised

'Thank God for women doctors!'
Thought Dot.'Who else would
prescribe a tub of chocolate
ice cream and a couple of days
in bed with the man
of your choice!'

'Of course I didn't burn my bra
when I was a girl.' Said Dot's
mother. 'It was made of
asbestos and reinforced steel.'

'He can't come to the phone!
Bellowed Dot.'He's helping
with the housework!'

Not to be outdone by Terry
ordering a 'Slow Screw Between
The Sheets', Dot ordered a
'Slow Screw Between The Sheets
With Two Complete Strangers
Wearing Rubber.'

'Just think, said Dot, in those days it was actually possible to find 3 wise men in one place.'

'Oh for God's sake!' Snapped Dot.
'Surely you've known me long
enough to know I mean right
when I say left.'

'I look younger?' Giggled Dot.
'Oh don't be silly, it takes
at least 30 years to
get as sexy as me!'

It started as a sexual experiment but soon Dot wanted Bruce to do everything 'doggie style'.

'For pity's sake', groaned Dot,
'a bunch of flowers and
a box of chocolates
would've been fine.'

'Mine or yours?' Asked Dot.

'It's amazing how this computer has captured your imagination,' said Dot, 'considering it doesn't have breasts or play football.'

'I think I've proved my point'. Said Dot.
'Give a man alcohol and promise
him sex and he'll do absolutely
anything! Right, home James-
to finish the washing-up.'

On the first day of her new job
Dot made a big impression on
the boss by inadvertently
sexually harassing him.

'I'll have the cream tea, please.'
Said Dot. 'And my sulky baboon
of a husband won't have anything,
because he lost the "pub or café"
argument.'

'Well', said Dot very calmly,
'if I'd known you were going to go
backwards, I wouldn't have opened
the sodding door.'

'Yes there is intelligent life
on Earth'. Replied Dot.
'You'll know it when you see it;
it'll be wearing make-up
and carrying something.'

Dot approached the man who
whistled at her: 'Normally I'd
punch you,' she growled, 'but it's
my 40th birthday today —
so I'll let you off.'

'Oh yes, he's a New Man
all right'. Said Dot. 'So new
I haven't even unwrapped
him yet.'

'Oi, John! It's a fax from that
Dot bird.' Shouted Gobby Dave,
'She says she's sorry for
calling you "titchynuts" and
can she see you tonight.'

'You've woken up with a headache?'
Crooned Dot.'Oh you poor love.'

'Ok!' Said Dot purposefully.
'I've sniffed the flowers and
eaten the chocolates. Now I
want to see some commitment!'

'You don't have to give me your seat because I'm a woman,' whispered Dot. 'You have to give it to me because I'm a working mother and I may go crazy if you don't.'

Dot reacted badly
when Dick announced
their relationship was over.

The men talked about fishing
and the women talked
about the men.

Dot decided to stick up for men:
'Of course men would be good at
having babies — they have
smaller brains so would
feel less pain.'

'All right,' agreed Dot reluctantly,
'it was better than a poke in the
eye with a sharp stick. But only
because it was quicker.'

'My politics are changing! Shouted
Dot.'I think a woman's place *is*
in the home-but a man's
is in the garden shed!'

'And that's the Women's Movement,
explained Dot; 'a sort of upward
jerk of the knee.'

'An aerobics video! For me?' Gasped Dot.
'Oh Barry, you shouldn't have.'

Dot was fed up with the childish
innuendo: 'Go on!' She snapped.
'Get your dick out and we'll
have an even bigger laugh!'

Gavin's behaviour became increasingly odd after he discovered Dot was earning more than him.

'I know my mental arithmetic
isn't as good as yours,'
said Dot, 'but I can afford
a bigger calculator than you.'

'Man overboard!' Shrieked Dot.
'Man overboard! Get the
champagne out!'

Sometimes Dot wanted
to hear 'delicious' instead of 'good'.

Dot arrived late at Roger's dinner party. She was determined to punish him for scoffing at her when she said she had nothing to wear.

'As the only other woman
in this office, you may have
already noticed that we're
surrounded by idiots'. Said Dot.

'No. I can't tonight, I'm
staying in to wash my hair'.
Said Dot. 'Tomorrow?
Er... look David, I'm washing
my hair one strand
at a time, ok.'

'Of course I haven't run out of petrol.' Giggled Dot. 'I'm just fed-up with his back-seat driving.'

'A snail farmer! Shrieked Dot,
wishing she'd never asked.
'Well, how... er... goodness... hmm...

It was one of life's
happy coincidences – Dot was
carrying some oven cleaner
when the flasher appeared.

'A bloody woman driver?
Correct!'. Said Dot drily.
'But do you know what this is?'

'You're telling me this doesn't
exploit women?! Gasped Dot.
'Oh sure, you can tell by the
way she polishes her uterus
she's a woman in control
of her life!'

Dot had to impress upon Gavin
that he couldn't just call
whenever he felt like it.

Dave didn't cook for Dot
very often and made
rather a performance
out of it when he did.

Dot couldn't get rid of
her past completely but
by ignoring Nigel, she
could reduce it to a
manageable level.

'I only asked for some
commitment for Chrissakes!'
Screamed Dot. 'Not your soul!'